For the Cartwheel team, with special appreciation to Orli Zuravicky,
Matt Ringler, and Jared Lee
—L.C.

To Jim and Darlene Barrett
—J.L.

ISBN 978-1-338-22789-5 • 10 9 8 7 6          18 19 20 21 22 • Printed in the U.S.A.    40 • First printing 2018

# THERE WAS AN OLD PIRATE WHO SWALLOWED A MAP!

by Lucille Colandro

illustrated by Jared Lee

Scholastic Inc.

There was an old pirate who swallowed a map.

I don't know why she swallowed the map —
*ARRR!* — but it wasn't a trap.

There was an old pirate who swallowed a line.
She had to recline when she swallowed the line.

She swallowed the line to hold the map.

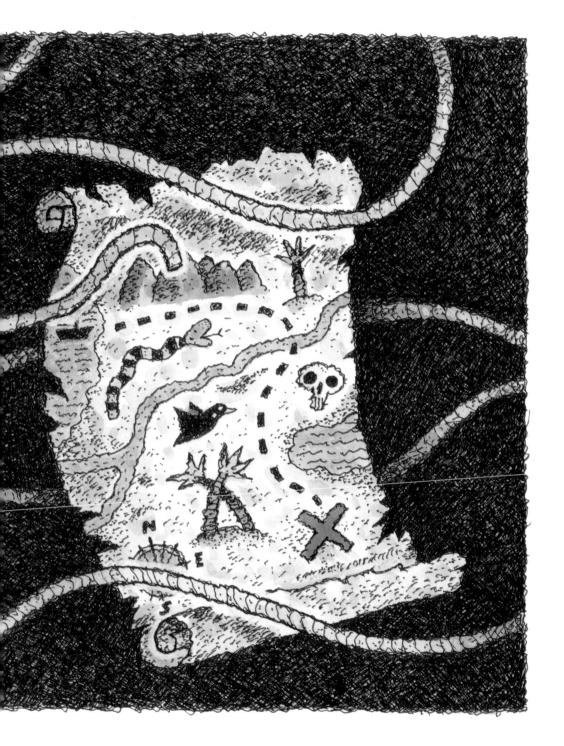

I don't know why she swallowed the map —
*ARRR!* — but it wasn't a trap.

There was an old pirate who swallowed a sword.
No one was bored when she swallowed her sword.

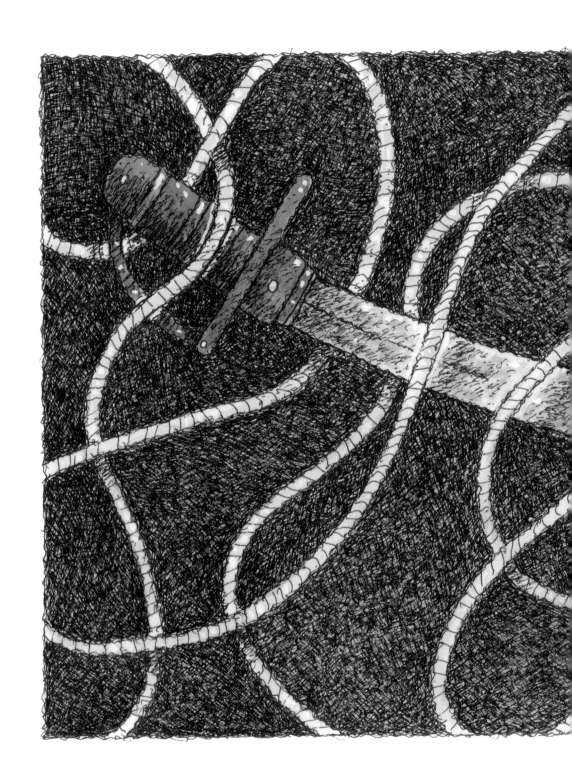

She swallowed the sword to cut the line.

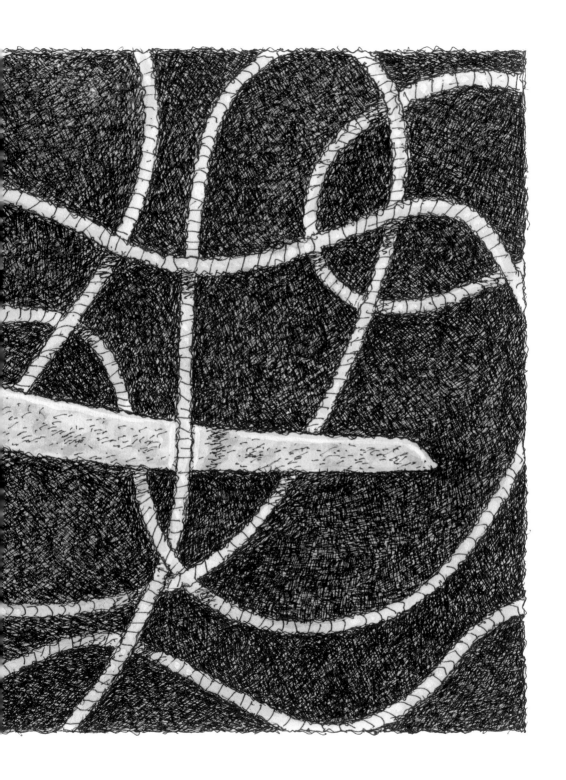

She swallowed the line to hold the map.

I don't know why she swallowed the map —

*ARRR!* — but it wasn't a trap.

There was an old pirate who swallowed a spyglass.

It was made of brass, that shiny spyglass.

She swallowed the spyglass to find the sword.

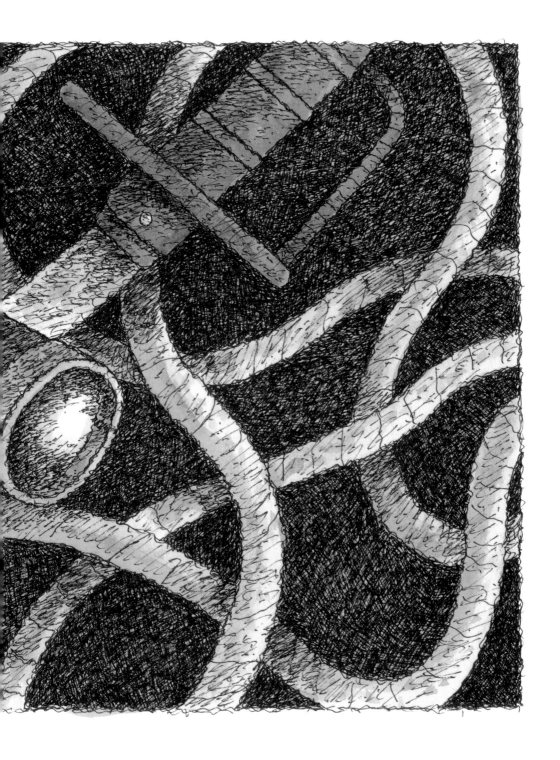

She swallowed the sword to cut the line.

She swallowed the line to hold the map.

I don't know why she swallowed the map —
*ARRR!* — but it wasn't a trap.

There was an old pirate who swallowed an anchor.
We all had to thank her
when she swallowed the anchor.

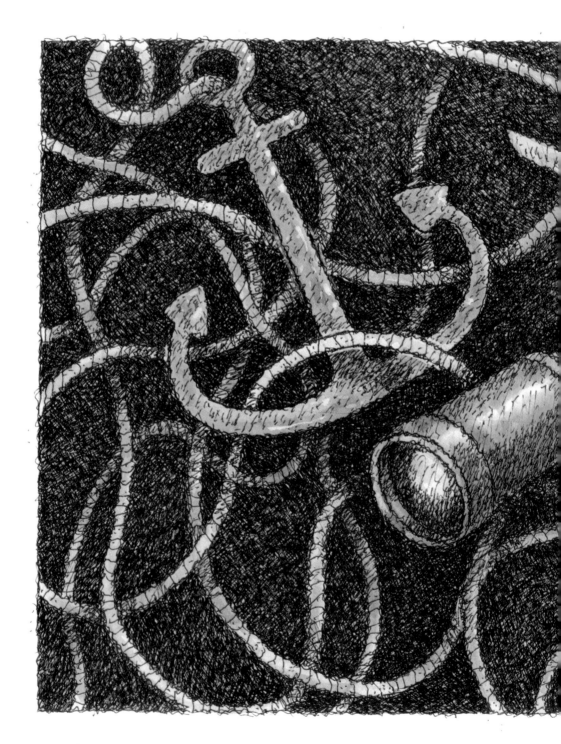

She swallowed the anchor to sink the spyglass.
She swallowed the spyglass to find the sword.

She swallowed the sword to cut the line.

She swallowed the line to hold the map.

I don't know why she swallowed the map —
*ARRR!* — but it wasn't a trap.

There was an old pirate who swallowed a flag.

She didn't gag when she swallowed that flag.

She swallowed the flag to cover the anchor.
She swallowed the anchor to sink the spyglass.

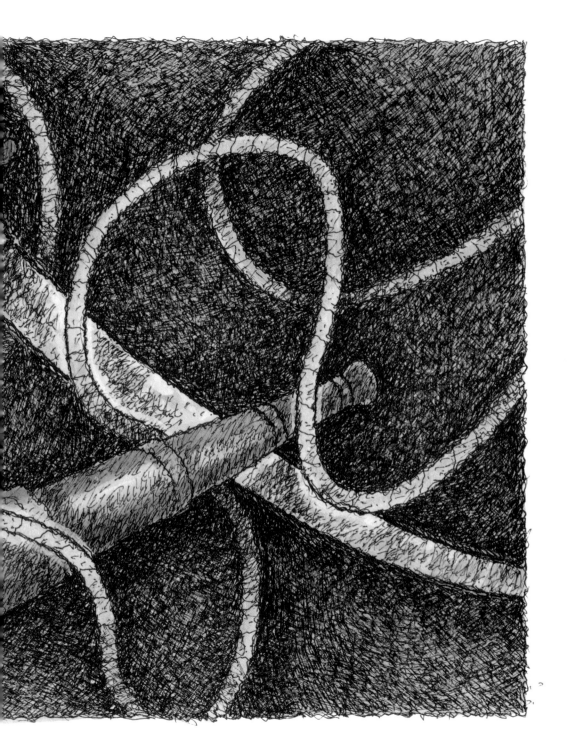

She swallowed the spyglass to find the sword.
She swallowed the sword to cut the line.

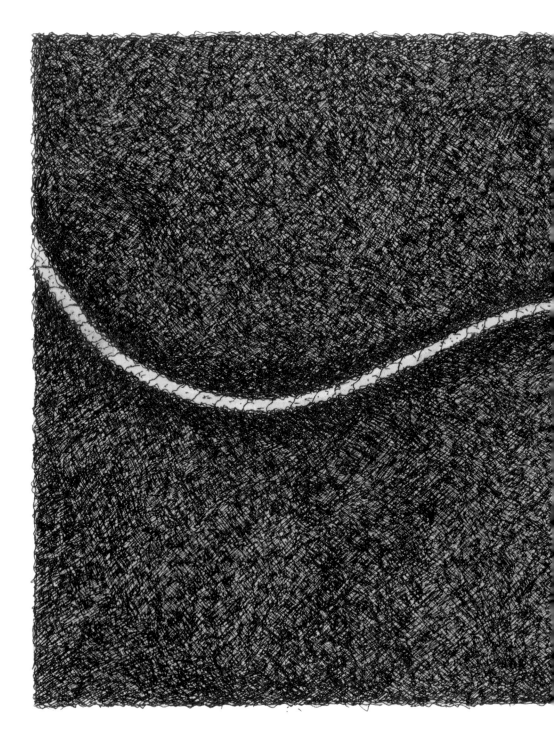

She swallowed the line to hold the map.

I don't know why she swallowed the map —
*ARRR!* — but it wasn't a trap.

There was an old pirate who swallowed a treasure.

It was a pleasure to swallow the treasure!

There was an old pirate who stayed until dark . . .

on the pirate ship ride at the amusement park.

55

Pirates rarely buried their treasure. They would split it up among themselves. Most of the money was spent quickly before they went looking for more! But books and movies still often show pirate **treasure maps** with riddles and an "*X* marks the spot."

The **spyglass** was first invented in the early 1600s. This handheld telescope used two lenses to magnify objects that were too far away to see. Pirates used spyglasses to spot land, seabirds, and other ships. Now we use powerful telescopes to see into space!

The rigging of a ship includes the sails, masts, and other ropes that help the ship move. When a rope is being used aboard a ship, it is called a **line**. Sailors and pirates would sometimes climb the ship's lines to reach the sails.

An **anchor** is a very heavy weight that drags in the sand to keep a ship from moving. The weight is often connected to the ship with an iron chain. Sailors originally used rocks to anchor their ships. Pirates would anchor their ships to climb aboard an enemy vessel!

Ships hung different-colored **flags** that meant different things. A red flag symbolized a battle. A black flag meant death. The most famous pirate flag is called the Jolly Roger. It shows a skull and crossbones.

Pirates often used a short, thick weapon called a cutlass. This **sword** had a slightly curved blade and often had a wide hilt to protect the owner's hand. A cutlass was strong enough to cut through heavy rigging on the ship, but short so that pirates could fight in small spaces.

# Search and Find!

The life of a sailor is full of adventure! Go back through the story and see if you can find the things listed below before the old pirate swallows them, too! When you've found them all, check your answers with the answer key at the bottom.

Happy searching!

*Some items appear on multiple pages; the answer key only lists the first page on which an item can be found.*

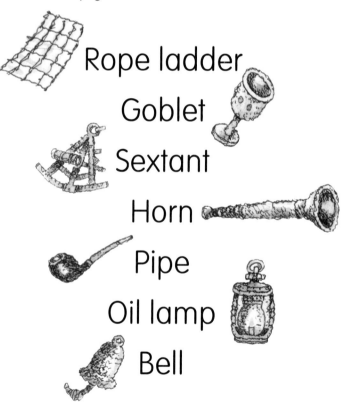

Rope ladder

Goblet

Sextant

Horn

Pipe

Oil lamp

Bell

Concertina

Clay jug

Ship wheel

Cannon

Barrel

Treasure chest

Hourglass

Candlestick

Monkey

Moon

Crown

Shovel

Parrot